Discover & Learn

Stone Age to Celts

Years 3-4

This Activity Book is full of sources and questions to help pupils in Years 3 and 4 explore the KS2 History topic 'Changes in Britain from the Stone Age to the Iron Age'.

Please note:
Pupils will need the matching CGP 'Stone Age to Celts' Study Book to answer the questions in this Activity Book.

History and Prehistory

We find out about history using <u>sources</u>. A <u>primary source</u> is something from the period we study. A <u>secondary source</u> is a record <u>about</u> a primary source.

Have a look at these sources. They're <u>tools</u> or <u>weapons</u> from the Stone Age.

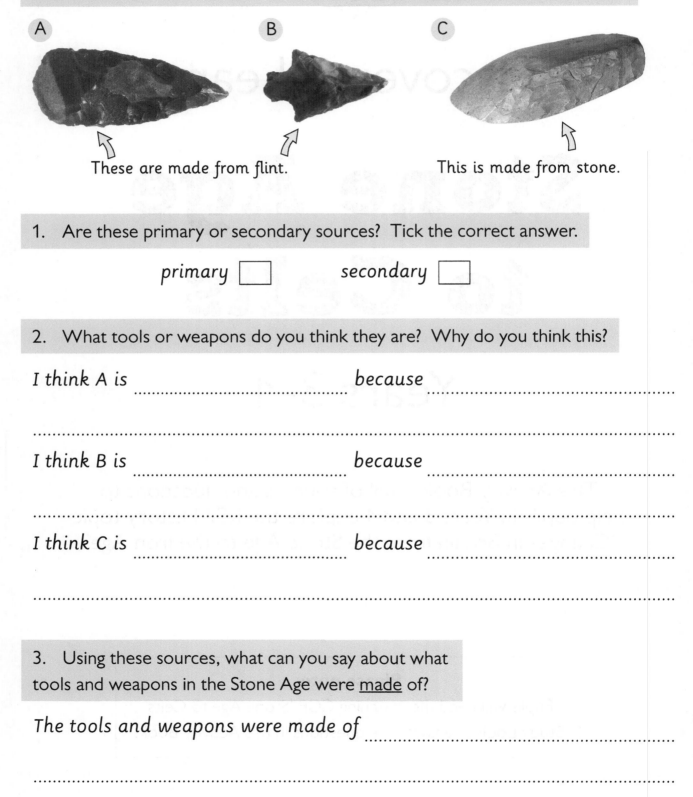

A   B   C

These are made from flint.   This is made from stone.

1. Are these primary or secondary sources? Tick the correct answer.

primary ☐   secondary ☐

2. What tools or weapons do you think they are? Why do you think this?

I think A is .... because ....

....

I think B is .... because ....

....

I think C is .... because ....

....

3. Using these sources, what can you say about what tools and weapons in the Stone Age were <u>made</u> of?

The tools and weapons were made of ....

....

Primary sources might not tell you the whole story.

The sources on page 2 give you information about what tools and weapons were used in the Stone Age.

4. Does this mean that these were the <u>only</u> tools and weapons used? Tick one box. Explain your answer.   Yes ☐   No ☐

I think this because ....

....

Read page 2 of the Study Book.

5. Apart from tools and weapons, what else might historians have found that tells them about life in Britain in the Stone Age?

Hint: In the Stone Age, people couldn't write.

They might have found ....

....

6. In this box, draw or write some things that historians in the future might discover from <u>our</u> time. What will it tell them about how we live?

What they might discover:	What it will tell them:
✏️	✏️

"I know that archaeologists and historians use primary and secondary sources to find out about the past."

How We Discover Prehistory

Most things that are made from <u>plants</u> and <u>animals</u> will <u>rot away</u> over time.

Many things that are <u>man-made</u> <u>will not rot away</u>.

For example, <u>wool</u> and <u>paper</u> will rot away. (Paper comes from trees.)

Things made of <u>plastic</u> and <u>glass</u> will <u>not rot away</u>.

Look around the room you are in. Think about all of the things in it. Now imagine the room being discovered in <u>10 000 years' time</u>. The building would have fallen down a long time ago, and been <u>buried</u> under soil and earth.

1.   What things in the room do you think would still be there for archaeologists to find? Explain why these things <u>would</u> survive.

I think that ....

....

because ....

....

2.   What things do you think <u>wouldn't</u> survive for archaeologists to find? Explain why not.

I think that ....

....

because ....

....

Some primary sources can be <u>misleading</u>...

The year is 12 050. An ancient classroom from 2014 has been discovered. Unexpectedly, a page of an exercise book has survived. Read what it says...

> ...Suddenly a huge asteroid struck the bridge of the spaceship. There was a loud crack, and all the lights flickered on and off.
>
> 'All officers to the stardrive section!' yelled the Captain, 'and turn on the force field!'

3. Tick 'Yes' or 'No' below to show which sentences you <u>agree</u> with.

The source proves that people in 2014 had spaceships. Yes ☐ No ☐

The source proves that people in 2014 wrote stories. Yes ☐ No ☐

The source proves nothing without other sources. Yes ☐ No ☐

4. Read page 5 of the Study Book. Explain how archaeologists can tell how old something is by how <u>deep</u> it is <u>buried</u>.

An archaeologist found a stone tool buried in the ground next to a <u>bone</u>.

5. How could the archaeologist find out how old the stone tool is?

"I understand how archaeologists and historians use sources, and why they must use them carefully."

The First People in Britain

The earliest evidence we've found of people living in Britain comes from Happisburgh. The people who lived there were different to humans today. Look at pages 6 and 7 of the Study Book to find out about them.

This picture shows a stretch of sand at the Happisburgh site and some footprints that were found there.

Historians think they were made by a group of people walking in the muddy shore of the river.

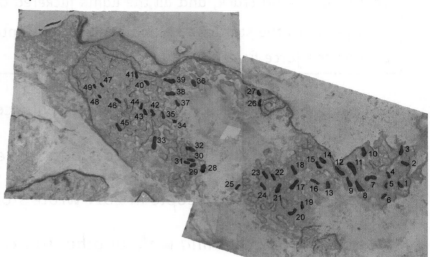

1. Write about daily life for the Happisburgh people. What do you think they were doing when the footsteps were made?

Use the picture and information in the Study Book to help you.

2. Write down four differences between you and the Happisburgh people.

1) ....

2) ....

3) ....

4) ....

3. List <u>three</u> things that you and the Happisburgh people have in <u>common</u>.

1) ....

2) ....

3) ....

The Happisburgh people may have left Britain because of a <u>glacial period</u>.
Look at page 7 of the Study Book to find out what a glacial period was like.

4. Think of a place in Britain that you know well. In the box below,
draw a picture of what it might have looked like in a <u>glacial period</u>.

> Think how this place would have been different in the glacial periods. What would have been there? What wouldn't have been there?

This is .... in the glacial periods.

5. Write down <u>two things</u> that scientists have studied that
have given them <u>evidence</u> that there were glacial periods.

1) ....

2) ....

"I know when the earliest evidence of people in Britain is from. I know what glacial periods are."

Early Humans in Britain

As the centuries went on, different groups of people lived in Britain.
Their lives were very <u>different</u> to <u>our lives</u> today.

Read the Fact File below.

<u>Boxgrove Fact File</u>

Climate: cool, damp

Animals to hunt: deer, wild horse, rhinoceros, elephant

Animals that hunted people: lion, hyena

Cooking: No evidence of cooked food.

Clothes: No evidence of clothing.

Houses: Perhaps used caves as shelters. No settlements.

Tools: Made of stone.

1. Use the Fact File and page 8 of the Study Book to write about a day in the life of the <u>Boxgrove people</u>.

In the morning we ....

....

At lunch time we ate ....

....

We were afraid of ....

....

At night we slept in ....

....

Scientists can tell a lot from a person's <u>skeleton</u>.

2.   Read page 9 of the Study Book. Write down how scientists can tell whether a skeleton belonged to a <u>man</u> or a <u>woman</u>.

3.   Tick the <u>two</u> things below that scientists can tell from a skeleton.

What type of clothes the person wore.   ☐

If the person was male or female.   ☐

What time of day the person died.   ☐

How long ago the person lived.   ☐

4.   Read about the <u>Pontnewydd</u> people on page 9 of the Study Book. If the Pontnewydd children came to <u>your</u> house today, what would amaze them?

Four things that they would be amazed by are:

1) ....

2) ....

3) ....

4) ....

"I can compare my life today with the lives of people who lived a long time ago."

Life in the Glacial Periods

Groups of people lived in Britain between glacial periods.

1.   Compare the people in the picture below with the <u>Happisburgh</u> people on page 6 of the Study Book. Do you think these people or the Happisburgh people were <u>more developed</u>? Explain why.

I think that .... *people were more*

developed because ....

....

....

During the glacial periods, people across Europe were creating <u>art</u>.

2.   Look at this example of cave art. What do you think it shows?

Around 33 000 years ago, <u>Paviland Man</u> died.

3. Look at page 10 of the Study Book. What <u>dangers</u> might Paviland man have faced in his life? What dangers do <u>you</u> face in your life?

Dangers in Paviland Man's life:	Dangers in my life:

4. Tick the sentence below that you <u>agree</u> with. Explain <u>why</u> you agree with it.

Paviland Man's life was more dangerous than my life is. ☐

My life is more dangerous than Paviland Man's life was. ☐

I think this because ....

....

Archaeologists think that the people who lived in the <u>Cheddar Caves</u> were <u>cannibals</u>.

5. Look at page 11 of the Study Book. In your own words say why archaeologists think that these people were <u>cannibals</u>.

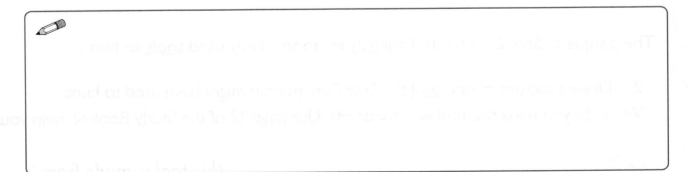

"I know what life was like for people who lived in Britain between 50 000 and 11 500 years ago."

The Mesolithic

By 11 500 years ago, the glacial periods were over and the Mesolithic began. One of the earliest settlements in Britain during the Mesolithic was at Star Carr, in Yorkshire.

The picture below shows what the huts at Star Carr may have been like.

Look at the picture and read the description below.

Floor: earth and clay, covered with reeds.

Roof: wood, thatched with reeds, turf, hides or bark.

Lighting: none

Toilets and bathroom: none

1.   What do you think it would have been like to live in a hut at Star Carr during the Mesolithic?

Write as much detail as you can about what you think it might have been like in the hut.

I think living in a hut at Star Carr would have been

....

....

....

....

The people at Star Carr hunted animals for food. They used tools to hunt.

2.   Draw a picture of one tool the Star Carr people might have used to hunt.
What do you think the tool was made of? Use page 12 of the Study Book to help you.

This tool is made from

....

....

3.   Read pages 12 and 13 of the Study Book then tick the correct boxes to show whether the sentences below are <u>true</u> or <u>false</u>.

	True	False
There were lots of forests in Britain in the Mesolithic.	☐	☐
People didn't use stone tools in the Mesolithic.	☐	☐
People ate deer, boar, fish, and beaver.	☐	☐
People used antler tools as well as stone tools.	☐	☐
People didn't travel around in the Mesolithic.	☐	☐
Mesolithic people might have had spiritual beliefs.	☐	☐

Manu lived at Star Carr with his family.

4.   Use pages 12 and 13 of your Study Book to write a short story about <u>a day in Manu's life</u>. Write about what he might have <u>seen</u>, <u>done</u> and <u>eaten</u> that day.

....

....

....

....

....

....

....

"I can imagine what life was like for someone who lived around 11 500 years ago."

Life in the Mesolithic

While Manu was living at Star Carr, other people were living in <u>different</u> parts of Britain, like Cheddar Gorge in Somerset. Their lives might have been quite <u>similar</u> to <u>each others' lives</u>, but they'd have been very <u>different</u> from <u>your</u> life...

Read p.14-15 of the Study Book to find out what Mesolithic people like Manu <u>ate</u>.

1. How would Manu's food have been different from yours?
Write a <u>menu</u> for <u>one day's food</u> for <u>you</u>, and a menu for one day for <u>Manu</u>.

Menu for me	Menu for Manu

Remember, Manu wouldn't have had any of these foods — potatoes, chicken, wheat, milk, butter, cheese or sugar (except wild honey).

2. What food that Manu ate would you like to try? What wouldn't you like to try?

I would like to try ....

because ....

I wouldn't like to try ....

because ....

The picture below shows a <u>cave</u> in Cheddar Gorge.
People lived in the caves in Cheddar Gorge during the Mesolithic.

3. Circle the words below that describe what <u>you</u>
think it would have been like to <u>live</u> in this cave.

Dark   Wet

     Scary

Safe   Light

   Warm   Cosy

    Exciting

4. Write one more word that describes
what it would be like to live in this cave. ....

Read page 15 of the Study Book. When people in the Mesolithic died, they were
sometimes buried with things that they <u>owned</u>.

5. What do you think Manu would have owned? He wouldn't have had
toys like yours, but what might he have had? Write or draw your answer.

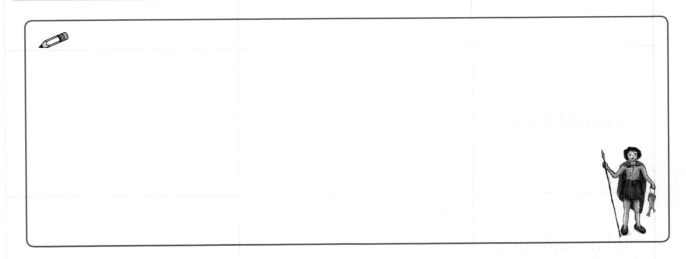

"I can compare my life with the life of someone
who lived around 11 500 years ago."

Changes in the Mesolithic

Archaeologists have found <u>footprints</u> on the coast at Goldcliff, in South Wales. They show that people walked there <u>7500 years ago</u>.

This picture shows what Goldcliff looks like <u>today</u>.

Imagine going for a walk in Goldcliff <u>today</u>, then imagine going for a walk in Goldcliff <u>7500 years ago</u>.

Look at page 16 of the Study Book to help you imagine Goldcliff 7500 years ago.

1. Complete the table below to say what <u>both</u> walks would be <u>like</u>.

	Today	7500 years ago
I would see...		
I would hear...		
Why might you be walking at the coast?		

2.   About 8200 years ago there was a <u>tsunami</u> in the North Sea.
Read page 17 of your Study Book then complete the sentences below.
Use the <u>key words</u> in the box to help you write the sentences.

Key Words

wave   collapsed   layer of sand   island

A tsunami is ....

The tsunami happened because ....

....

We know there was a tsunami because ....

....

....

After the tsunami, Britain ....

....

3.   Imagine you were safe and <u>watching</u> the tsunami from a distance. What do
you think you would have <u>seen</u> and <u>heard</u>? Write or draw your ideas in the box.

"I know that things change over time and that some
changes can happen quickly and have a big effect."

The Neolithic

After the Mesolithic came the Neolithic. Read pages 18-19 of the Study Book to find out the differences between life in the Mesolithic and life in the Neolithic.

1.   For each sentence below, decide whether the person speaking lived during the Mesolithic or the Neolithic. If the speaker is Mesolithic colour the speech bubble in blue. If the speaker is Neolithic colour the speech bubble in red.

I move from place to place with my family. We never stay in the same place for long.

I own pottery jars of different sizes — they're really useful.

I have a cloak made from woven cloth.

All of my clothes are made from animal skins.

My family grows crops for food.

I live in a town with my family. We stay there all year round.

I hunt animals for food and I gather food wherever I can find it. I don't grow any food myself.

2.   Why did Neolithic people domesticate animals? Give two reasons. Use page 18 of the Study Book to help you.

1) ....

2) ....

People started <u>farming</u> in the Neolithic.

	True	False
Farming started in Britain about 50 000 years ago.	☐	☐
Some farmers may have come from abroad.	☐	☐
Some people caught diseases from the animals.	☐	☐
The more people there are, the more land is needed for farming.	☐	☐

4. Would <u>you</u> rather have been alive during the <u>Mesolithic</u> or the <u>Neolithic</u>? Why? You may want to use some of the words in the box in your answer.

| farming   animals   town   disease   fighting   pottery |

These words are here to help you, but you don't need to use them all.

I would rather have been alive in the ....

because ....

....

....

....

....

....

"I know the differences between life in the Mesolithic and life in the Neolithic."

Neolithic Village Life

Neolithic life was more <u>settled</u> than Mesolithic life. People didn't travel as much because they had to look after animals and crops.

"My name is Vali. I live at Skara Brae, in one of the stone houses."

Read pages 20 and 21 of the Study Book to find out what life was like at Skara Brae. Think about how this was different to how your life is.

1. What do you have to do each day? How would Vali's day have been different?

Every day I have to ....

....

....

Vali's day would be different because ....

....

....

2. Look at the picture below. These strange objects were found at Skara Brae. Archaeologists aren't sure what they are. What do <u>you</u> think they are?

On page 20 of the Study Book there's a photograph of
the remains of a house at Skara Brae.

3.   Draw and label a picture of what you think the <u>inside</u>
of the house looked like when Vali was alive. Use the
photograph and other information on the page to help you.

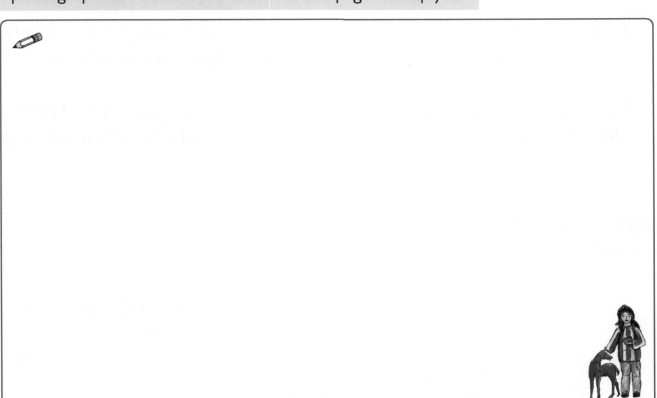

4.   Look at the pictures below. Do you think picture A or picture B shows
Neolithic tools? Why do you think this? Use page 21 of the Study Book to help you.

Picture ....

shows Neolithic tools.

I can tell because ....

....

"I know about daily life during the Neolithic."

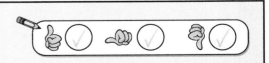

Neolithic Stone Circles

Historians think people began to keep track of <u>time</u>, like the changing <u>seasons</u>, during the Neolithic. <u>Stone circles</u> may have been built to help them do this.

1. Why was it important to know when the <u>seasons</u> would <u>change</u> in the Neolithic? Circle the correct answer below. Use page 22 of the Study Book to help you.

So you knew when Christmas was.

So you knew what clothes you needed.

So you knew when to plant and harvest crops.

<u>Stonehenge</u> is a Neolithic stone circle. Neolithic people travelled long distances to visit Stonehenge.

Some of the stones are over 6 metres tall — that's 4 times taller than an average woman.

2. Imagine you were a <u>visitor</u> to Stonehenge in Neolithic times. Write a description of what it would have been like. Use pages 22 and 23 of the Study Book and the picture above to help you.

3. Draw a circle around the sentences below that you think are <u>correct</u>.
Use pages 22 and 23 of the Study Book if you need help.

Durrington Walls was a
village near Stonehenge.

The winter and summer solstices were
important days to Neolithic people.

The longest day of the
year is the winter solstice.

Stonehenge wasn't in Britain.

Knowing when the summer and winter
solstices were was important for farming.

Archaeologists have found evidence that some Neolithic people celebrated the
winter solstice with a <u>feast</u> near Stonehenge.

4. Imagine you travelled back in time to the winter solstice 4500 years ago.
Write or draw what you might have seen happening.

"I know that Neolithic people built stone circles and
understand some reasons why they built them."

Flint, Copper and Bronze

In the Neolithic, people mined <u>flint</u> to make tools from. People still mine for things these days. The picture below shows some people down a mine <u>today</u>.

Look at this picture.
Now read about Neolithic mining and look at the picture of the mine on page 24 of your Study Book.

1. Do you think mining is more or less dangerous <u>today</u>, than it was in the <u>Neolithic</u>? Explain your answer.

I think that mining .... *more dangerous because*

....

....

....

....

Historians think that <u>children</u> would have been sent down the mines because they could get into the <u>smallest tunnels</u>.

2. Look at page 24 of the Study Book. Imagine you worked down the mines. In the box below write or draw what you think it would have been like.

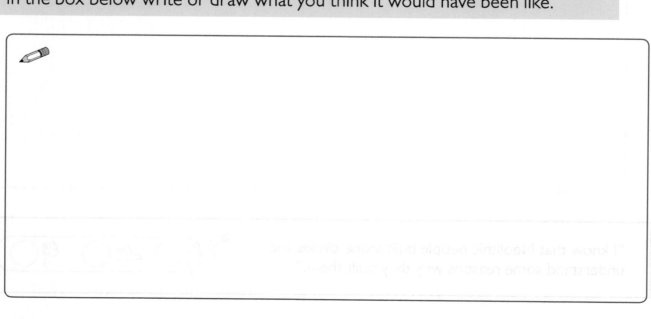

At the end of the Neolithic, people in Britain started to make tools and weapons out of <u>copper</u>.

3. Read page 25 of your Study Book then tick the correct boxes to show whether the sentences below are <u>true</u> or <u>false</u>.

	True	False
People in Britain made tools out of copper 20 000 years ago.	☐	☐
People who made copper tools could swap them for things that they needed.	☐	☐
Copper is a type of rock.	☐	☐
The Stone Age ended when people started making tools from metal.	☐	☐
You need to melt copper to shape it into tools and weapons.	☐	☐
The people of Britain were the first people to discover how to make tools out of copper.	☐	☐

The <u>Bronze Age</u> in Britain started about <u>4000 years ago</u>. It's when people started to make things out of <u>bronze</u>. Look at page 25 of the Study Book.

4. What is bronze a mixture of? Tick <u>two</u> boxes.

flint ☐   copper ☐

gold ☐   tin ☐

5. Why did people start to make things out of bronze instead of copper?

People started making things out of bronze because ....

....

"I know about flint mining and I understand how the use of copper and bronze developed."

Life After the Stone Age

Some of the remains found near <u>Stonehenge</u> tell us that people <u>travelled</u> — people who were alive just after the Stone Age came from all over Europe to visit Stonehenge.

1. Why do you think people travelled to Stonehenge from different countries? Why do people travel to different countries today?

People travelled to Stonehenge because ....

....

....

Today people travel to different countries to ....

....

....

Read about the <u>Boscombe Bowmen</u> on page 27 of the Study Book.

2. Where do archaeologists think the Boscombe Bowmen came from?

Archaeologists think they came from ....

3. In the box on the right, draw one of the things found in the grave that gave the Boscombe Bowmen their <u>name</u>. What do you think this object was made of?

The thing I've drawn is made of:

....

Read about the <u>Amesbury Archer</u> and his <u>companion</u> on pages 26 and 27 of the Study Book.

4.   Draw a picture of what you think the Archer would have looked like in the box below. Then, imagine that you are the Archer telling someone the story of your life. Write down what you would say to them.

I am the Archer. I was born ....

....

....

....

....

....

....

5.   Now do the same for the companion...

For your pictures, think about what they might have worn and carried with them.

I am the companion. I was raised in ....

....

....

....

....

....

....

"I know that people who were alive just after the Stone Age travelled to places that were important to them."

Bronze Age Travel and Trade

In the Bronze Age there was a difference between the <u>rich</u> and the <u>poor</u>.

1. For each speech bubble below, decide whether the Bronze Age person speaking is more likely to be rich or poor. Write your answer under each speech bubble.

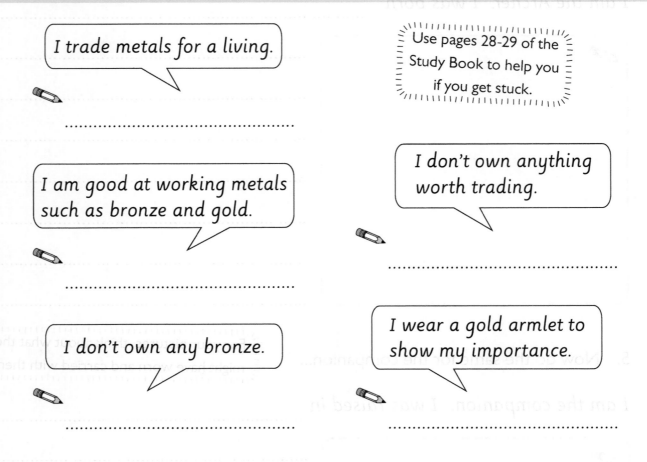

I trade metals for a living.

....

Use pages 28-29 of the Study Book to help you if you get stuck.

I am good at working metals such as bronze and gold.

....

I don't own anything worth trading.

....

I don't own any bronze.

....

I wear a gold armlet to show my importance.

....

Look at the <u>cape</u> on page 29 of your Study Book.

2. Imagine you were the person who owned it. What do you think your life would have been like? Do you think you lived well? Write your ideas in the box below.

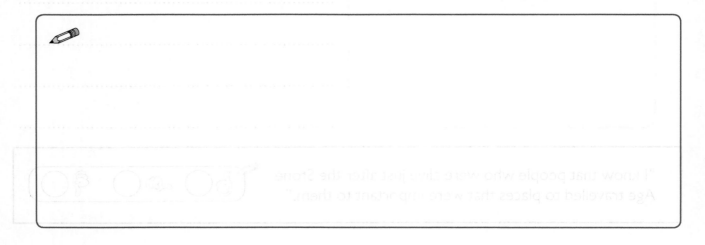

The picture below shows men <u>farming</u> the land.

3. Look at the picture of the men on page 28 of your Study Book.
Which men do you think were <u>richer</u>? Explain your answer.

I think that the men .... *were richer because*

....

....

Read page 29 of your Study Book.

4. Read the sentences below. Circle the ones that you think are <u>true</u>.

Archaeologists think the amber necklace was from Wales.

Archaeologists sometimes use people's teeth to work out where they were from.

People from abroad brought new ways of working metal to Britain.

Archaeologists think the boy with the amber necklace was from Stonehenge.

"I know that in the Bronze Age some people were rich and some were poor and I understand why."

Life in the Bronze Age

In the Bronze Age, people <u>travelled</u> on <u>foot</u> and by <u>boat</u>. Some historians think that they might have begun to use <u>horses</u> to travel around too.

1. Give <u>two</u> ways that humans might have used <u>horses</u> for travelling in the Bronze Age.

1) ....

....

....

2) ....

....

> Think about how humans could have used horses to get around, and how they could have used horses to move their things around.

Dhu lived at <u>Must Farm</u> in the Fens. Read what he has to say.

"I live with my family in a hut. My father is a bronzesmith. I help look after our animals and crops. My mother weaves our clothes out of wool."

Use pages 30-31 of the Study Book to help you answer these questions.

2. What do you think Dhu's sword and shield are made of? Tick the box.

iron ☐   stone ☐   bronze ☐

3. What do you think Dhu's mother uses to weave clothes?

....

Life had changed a lot in the 8000 years since the <u>Mesolithic</u> began. Look back at what you wrote about <u>Manu's life</u> in the Mesolithic on pages 12-15 of this book.

4.   In the box below, write how Manu's life was different from <u>Dhu's</u>. Think about things like what they both wore, what they ate and what they would have spent their days doing. Use pages 30-31 of the Study Book to help you.

Manu's life

Dhu's life

5.   Would you rather have lived as Manu did or as Dhu lived? Explain why.

I would rather have lived like .... *because* ....

....

....

....

"I know what daily life was like in the Bronze Age and I know how people travelled."

The End of the Bronze Age

By the <u>end</u> of the Bronze Age, the <u>weather</u> in Britain had <u>changed</u> a lot.
Read page 32 of your Study Book.

1.   Imagine you are living in Britain towards the end of the Bronze Age. Write a <u>weather forecast</u> describing what the weather will be like for the <u>next three days</u>.

2.   Archaeologists believe that Bronze Age people made <u>offerings</u> to the water spirits and gods. Read page 32 of your Study Book. In the box below draw a picture of people making offerings. <u>Label</u> your drawing to explain what it shows.

3.   What <u>evidence</u> do you think archaeologists have for thinking that people made offerings to water spirits?

Hint: What do you think they might have found?

....

....

People began to farm in <u>hillforts</u> towards the end of the Bronze Age.

4. Use page 33 of the Study Book to help you draw a hillfort. Label the different parts of your picture to show what they are and what they are made from.

Towards the end of the Bronze Age, people started making <u>alliances</u> and living in <u>tribes</u>. Read pages 32 and 33 of your Study Book.

Think about what advantages this would have given people over just living with their families.

5. Why do you think people started doing this?

....

....

....

....

"I know what life was like in Britain towards the end of the Bronze Age."

The Celtic Age of Iron

Historians think that people in Britain first started using <u>iron</u> about 2700 years ago.
Read page 34 of your Study Book.

1. Why might people have started using iron instead of bronze?

....

....

Iron gradually <u>rusts</u> away when it comes into contact with air and water.
The sickle and sword found at Llyn Fawr are from about <u>2700 years ago</u> —
they are some of the <u>earliest</u> examples of iron found in Britain.

2. Do you think people in Britain used iron <u>before 2700 years ago</u>?
Tick the sentence below that you <u>agree</u> with. Explain <u>why</u> you agree with it.

People in Britain definitely didn't use iron before 2700 years ago. ☐

People in Britain definitely used iron before 2700 years ago. ☐

People in Britain could have used iron before 2700 years ago. ☐

I think this because ....

....

People living in the <u>Iron Age</u> are often known as <u>Celts</u>.

3. Read page 35 of your Study Book. Tick the correct boxes
to show whether the sentences below are <u>true</u> or <u>false</u>.

	True	False
There were no Celtic tribes outside of Britain.	☐	☐
The Celts were made up of lots of different tribes.	☐	☐
The Caledones were a Celtic tribe from Scotland.	☐	☐
The Iceni are an example of a Celtic tribe.	☐	☐

Look at the <u>map</u> showing where the Celtic tribes lived on page 35 of your Study Book.

4.   Which of these tribes lived closest to where you live?

The tribe that lived closest to me is the .... *tribe.*

Look at the picture of the Iron Age family on page 35 of your Study Book.

5.   In the boxes below, describe the <u>differences</u> between an Iron Age family and your family. Think about <u>where they live</u>. Look at the things they're <u>doing</u>. What <u>different</u> things do you and your family do when you're at home?

Iron Age Family	My Family

6.   Are there any <u>similarities</u> between your family and the Iron Age family? List as many as you can.

....

....

....

"I know about the use of iron in the Iron Age, and I know who the Celts were."

Life in the Iron Age

Danebury Hillfort was an <u>Iron Age hillfort</u>.
Fifion lives at <u>Danebury Hillfort</u>. Read what she has to say.

> *"I live and work with my family in the hillfort.*
> *We are kept busy with the farming. Life is good, but*
> *we worry about being attacked by other tribes."*

1.   In the box below, write a <u>story</u> set in Danebury Hillfort.
Make Fifion the <u>main character</u> in your story. Try and make
your story as <u>descriptive</u> and <u>exciting</u> as you can.
Use pages 36 and 37 of the Study Book to help you.

9

2. What evidence of fighting have archaeologists found at Danebury Hillfort? Use page 37 of your Study Book to help you.

....

....

The picture below shows the remains of a hillfort.

3. Do you think a hillfort would be easy or hard to <u>attack</u>? Why?

I think a hillfort would be ....
to attack because ....

....

....

....

....

Look at the sword on page 37 of the Study Book.

4. Draw what you think the sword would have looked like when it was <u>new</u>. Write <u>four</u> words that would have described the sword when it was new.

1) .... 3) ....

2) .... 4) ....

"I know that life in Britain was sometimes peaceful and sometimes violent during the Iron Age."

An Invasion from Rome

Life in Britain <u>changed</u> a lot when the <u>Romans</u> arrived.

1. Read page 38 of your Study Book, then fill in the gaps in the sentences below.

The city of Rome is in .... *. By about 2250 years*

ago, the Romans were starting to build an .... *.*

Around 2060 years ago, a Roman leader called ....

tried to conquer Gaul completely.

Have a look at pages 38 and 39 of your Study Book.

2. Give <u>two</u> reasons why Julius Caesar wanted to invade Britain.

1) ....

....

2) ....

....

Read the sentence below.

> *"History began in Britain when the Romans arrived."*

3. Read page 39 of your Study Book.
Tick the sentence below that explains why the sentence above is <u>true</u>.

Exciting things started happening once the Romans came to Britain. ☐

It's when BC and AD dating was first used in Britain. ☐

It's when people in Britain started writing things down. ☐

Read about BC and AD dating on page 39 of your Study Book.

4. Fill in the gaps in the sentences below.

BC stands for ....

AD stands for ....

The year I was born in was ....

Include <u>BC</u> or <u>AD</u> with your answer to this question.

5. Tick the correct boxes to show whether the sentences below are <u>true</u> or <u>false</u>.

	True	False
The year 100 BC came after AD 70.	☐	☐
The year AD 1000 came before AD 800.	☐	☐
The year 90 BC came after 200 BC.	☐	☐
AD 2000 is 2000 years after Jesus Christ is thought to have been born.	☐	☐

6. Write the letters of the events below in the correct boxes on the timeline, to show when they happened. One has been done for you.

A — Julius Caesar tried to conquer Gaul.
B — The start of the Iron Age in Britain.
C — The start of the Bronze Age in Britain.
D — Now
E — Building of Stonehenge started.

You might have to look back in the Study Book to help you.

E	☐	☐	☐	☐

4000 BC   2000 BC   AD 1   AD 2000

"I know some reasons why the Romans wanted to invade Britain. I can use BC and AD correctly."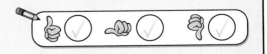

Picture acknowledgements

Cover photo (hillfort) Private Collection / © English Heritage Photo Library / Bridgeman Images.

Thumb illustration used throughout the book © iStockphoto.com

p2 (tool A) © iStockphoto.com/MarVal.

p2 (tool B) © iStockphoto.com/lucamanieri.

p2 (tool C) © iStockphoto.com/Laurentius.

p4 (jumper) © iStockphoto.com/mattjeacock.

p7 (Happisburgh site) © 2014 Ashton et al. http://www.plosone.org/article/info%3Adoi%2F10.1371%2Fjournal.pone.0088329 licenced for re-use under the creative commons licence http://creativecommons.org/licenses/by/4.0/.

p10 (cave scene) © Mary Evans/Fonollosa/Iberfoto.

p10 (cave painting) © Iberfoto/Mary Evans.

p12 (hut) © iStockphoto.com/TT.

p15 (cave) A chamber and mirror pool inside Gough's Cave, Cheddar, called Alladdin's Cave by Rwendland licenced for re-use under the creative commons licence, http://creativecommons.org/licenses/by-sa/3.0/deed.en.

p16 (Goldcliff) © David Williams / Alamy.

p20 (carved objects) © National Museums Scotland.

p21 (A) © Royal Albert Memorial Museum, Exeter, Devon, UK / Bridgeman Images.

p21 (B) © Mary Evans/M.C.Esteban/Iberfoto.

p29 (farming) Private Collection / © Look and Learn / Bridgeman Images.

p37 (hillfort) Werner Forman Archive / Bridgeman Images.